Fables for Children

Aesop

Condensed and Adapted by
KATHRYN KNIGHT

Illustrated by
MILO WINTER

Cover Illustrated by
MILO WINTER

Dalmatian Press

The Junior Classics have been
adapted and illustrated with care and thought
to introduce you to a world of famous authors, characters, ideas,
and great stories that have been loved for generations.

Editor — Kathryn Knight
Creative Director — Gina Rhodes Haynes
And the entire classics project team
of Dalmatian Publishing Group

FABLES FOR CHILDREN

A note to the reader—

A book of classic fables rests in your hands. The characters are famous. The tales are timeless.

This Junior Classic edition of *Fables for Children* by Aesop has been carefully condensed and adapted from older versions that have been handed down from generation to generation. Whether Aesop was actually the father of Greek fables, or whether these tales were simply collected from several sources through the years, these fables have stood the test of time. For centuries, they have been told and retold, written and rewritten, edited and illustrated, both for entertainment and education. The fables of Aesop may date back to the 6th century BC, but they are part of modern literature and learning.

> *It all depends on the point of view,*
> *and who tells the story.* — Aesop

Curl up and enjoy.

Was Aesop a real person? Historians are not sure. Did a Greek slave really create fables about a tortoise and a bragging hare? or a fox and some juicy-looking grapes that were just out of reach? Or did other writers of long ago make up these fables that carry Aesop's name?

According to legend, Aesop was born a slave about 620 BC, either in Greece or Ethiopia in Africa. (The name Aesop comes from an ancient Greek word for Ethiop.) He was said to be rather ugly, with rough skin, a hunchback, a flat nose, a crooked body, and an oddly shaped head. But Aesop had a talent for telling stories that taught valuable lessons. He was known for his clever wit and wisdom, and this earned him his freedom.

Aesop loved to teach and travel. He became a special assistant and speaker for Croesus, the wealthy king of Lydia. He was sent to deliver gold to the ruler of the city of Delphi in Greece. Unfortunately, it was here that Aesop lost his life. According to some stories, the great fable-teller refused to deliver Croesus's gold, because he felt that the people and ruler of Delphi were much too greedy. This made the people very angry, and Aesop was put to death.

Aesop
Painted by Diego Velázquez about 1640

After his death, Aesop's popular fables were passed down from parents to children for hundreds of years. They were not written down at first, but were eventually recorded in written form. These famous fables have now been translated into many different languages. Children all over the world recognize the name of one of the world's greatest storytellers— Aesop, a man who may have been real, or may have lived only in the imaginations of storytellers of long, long ago.

Fables for Children

The Fox and the Stork

The Fox often teased the Stork about his very long legs and bill. And one day the Fox thought of a way to amuse himself with the Stork.

"You must come and have dinner with me tomorrow," he said to the Stork, smiling to himself at the trick he was going to play.

The Stork happily accepted and arrived the next day, quite hungry indeed.

For dinner the Fox served soup. But it was set out in a very shallow dish. All the Stork could do was wet the very tip of his bill. Not a drop of soup could he get. But the Fox lapped it up easily.

"Oh, isn't this tasty!" said the ~~Fox~~ "I do hope you are enjoying your meal."

But of course the hungry ~~Stork~~ was not enjoying the meal at all. He was quite displeased at the trick, but he was a calm fellow. He knew there was no good in flying into a rage.

"Thank you, kind friend," said the ~~Stork~~, turning to leave. "The soup was indeed tasty."

Not long afterward, the ~~Stork~~ invited the ~~Fox~~ to his home for dinner. The ~~Fox~~ arrived eagerly.

"I'm so hungry!" he said. "Do I smell fish?"

"Yes, a fine fish dinner," said the ~~Stork~~.

The ~~Stork~~ brought out the fish dinner—but it was served in a tall jar with a very narrow neck. The ~~Stork~~ could easily get at the food with his long bill. All the ~~Fox~~ could do was lick the outside of the jar and sniff at the delicious odor.

When the ~~Fox~~ lost his temper, the ~~Stork~~ said calmly:

> *Do not play tricks on your neighbors*
> *unless you can stand the same treatment yourself.*

Belling the Cat

The Mice once called a meeting to decide on a plan to free themselves of their enemy, the Cat. They wished to find some way of knowing when she was coming, so they might have time to run away. Indeed, something had to be done, for they lived in constant fear of her claws. The Mice hardly dared to stir from their dens by night or day.

Many plans were discussed, but none of them was thought good enough. At last a very young Mouse got up and said:

"I have a plan that seems simple, but I know it will work. All we have to do is hang a bell about the Cat's neck. When we hear the bell ringing, we will know immediately that our enemy is coming."

All the Mice were surprised that they had not thought of such a plan before. But as they clapped and rejoiced, an old Mouse arose and said:

"I will say that the plan sounds very good. But let me ask one question: Who will bell the Cat?"

It is one thing to say that something should be done, but quite a different matter to do it.

The Raven and the Swan

A Raven wanted the snowy feathers of a Swan. "I will live like a Swan, swimming and diving all day," he said. "I will eat the plants that grow in the water, and surely I will become a Swan."

So he left his home in the fields and flew down to live on a lake. But though he tried to swim and dive, he nearly drowned. And the water plants he ate did not agree with him. So he got thinner and thinner, and at last he died.

A change of habits will not alter nature.

The Dog, the Rooster, and the Fox

A Dog and a Rooster, who were the best of friends, wished very much to see something of the world. So they decided to leave the farmyard and set out into the world along the road that led to the woods. The two friends traveled along in the very best of spirits and without meeting any adventure to speak of.

At nightfall the Rooster looked for a place to roost. He spied nearby a hollow tree that he thought would do nicely for a night's sleep. The Dog crept inside, and the Rooster flew up onto one of the branches. Both slept very comfortably.

With the first glimmer of dawn, the Rooster awoke. For the moment he forgot just where he was. He thought he was still in the farmyard where it had been his duty to awaken the household at daybreak. So, standing on tiptoes, he flapped his wings and crowed loudly. But instead of awakening the farmer, he awakened a Fox not far off in the woods.

The Fox immediately had thoughts of a delicious breakfast. He hurried to the tree where the Rooster was roosting and said very politely:

"Welcome to our woods, dear sir. I cannot tell you how glad I am to see you here. I am quite sure we shall become the closest of friends. Please, sir, fly down here next to me so that we may get to know each other better."

"How kind of you, sir," replied the Rooster slyly. "Please, do come up here instead. If you will go around to the door of my house at the foot of the tree, my butler will let you in."

The hungry Fox did not suspect a trick, and he went around the tree as he was told. In a twinkling the Dog leaped out and made an end to him.

Those who try to trick others
may find themselves tricked instead.

The Lion and the Mouse

A Lion lay asleep in the forest, with his great head resting on his paws. A little Mouse came along and ran over his nose, which woke the Lion. The angry Lion laid his huge paw on the tiny Mouse and was about to kill him.

"Oh, please," begged the poor Mouse, "if you will let me go, I promise to repay you in some way."

The Lion laughed at the idea that a little Mouse could ever repay him, but he let him go.

It happened shortly after this that the Lion was caught by some hunters, who tied him with strong ropes to the ground. The Mouse, hearing his roar, came and chewed through the rope with his teeth and set him free.

"Was I not right?" said the little Mouse.

Little friends may prove to be great friends.

The Young Crab and His Mother

"Why in the world do you walk sideways like that?" said a Mother Crab crossly to her son. "You should always walk straight forward with your toes turned out."

"Oh, please show me how to walk, Mother dear," answered the little Crab. "I want to learn."

So the old Crab tried and tried to walk straight forward. But no matter how hard she tried, she could only walk sideways, like her son. And when she wanted to turn her toes out, she tripped and fell on her nose.

Do not tell others how to act
unless you can set a good example.

The Frog and the Ox

An Ox came down to a pond to drink. As he splashed heavily into the water, he crushed a young Frog into the mud. The old Mother Frog soon missed the little one and asked his brothers and sisters what had become of him.

"A great big, big monster," said one of them, "stepped on little brother with one of his huge, big, big feet."

"Big, was he," said the old Frog, puffing herself up. "Was he as big as this?"

"Oh, much bigger," they cried.

The Frog puffed up still more. "Well, he could not have been bigger than this," she said.

But the little Frogs all declared that the monster was much, much bigger, and the old Frog kept puffing herself out more and more until, all at once, she burst.

Do not attempt the impossible.

The Boy and the Figs

A greedy Boy thrust his hand into a jar to get some figs. But he took such a great fistful that he could not get his hand out again. There he stood, unwilling to give up a single fig, yet unable to get them all out at once. So he began to cry.

"My boy," said his mother, "be satisfied with half the figs you have taken and you will easily get your hand out. Then perhaps you may have some more figs some other time."

Do not attempt too much at once.

The Wild Boar and the Fox

A Wild Boar was busy sharpening his tusks against the stump of a tree. A Fox walked by. Now, the Fox was always looking for a chance to fool a neighbor. So he began to look back over his shoulder in fear, as if an enemy were close by. But the Boar kept right on with his work.

"Why are you doing that?" asked the Fox at last with a grin. "There isn't any danger that I can see."

"True," replied the Boar. "But when danger *does* come, there will not be time to sharpen my tusks. My weapons must always be ready to use."

Always be prepared.

The Town Mouse
and the Country Mouse

A Town Mouse once visited a cousin who lived in the country. For lunch the Country Mouse served wheat stalks, roots, and acorns, with a dash of cold water for drink. The Town Mouse ate very little, nibbling a little of this and a little of that. She made it very plain that she ate the simple food only to be polite.

After the meal, the friends had a long talk—or rather the Town Mouse talked about her life in the city while the Country Mouse listened. They then went to bed in a cozy nest tucked away in a haybale and slept in quiet and comfort until morning.

In her sleep the Country Mouse dreamed she was a Town Mouse with all the fancy foods and delights of city life that her cousin had described for her. So the next day when the Town Mouse asked the Country Mouse to go home with her to the city, she gladly said yes.

When they reached the mansion in which the Town Mouse lived, they found on the table in the dining room the leftovers of a very fine banquet.

There were jellies, pastries, delicious cheeses—the most tempting foods a Mouse can imagine. But just as the Country Mouse was about to nibble a dainty bit of pastry, she heard a Cat meow loudly and scratch at the door.

In great fear, the Mice scurried to a hiding place, where they lay quite still for a long time. They hardly dared to breathe. When at last they crept back to the feast, the door opened suddenly. In came many servants, followed by the big House Dog.

The Country Mouse stopped in the Town Mouse's den only long enough to pick up her carrying case and umbrella.

"You may have rich foods that I have not," she said as she hurried away, "but I prefer my plain food and simple life in the country with the peace and safety that go with it."

It is better to live simply and safely
than to live with riches and fear.

The Fox and the Grapes

A Fox one day spied a beautiful bunch of ripe grapes hanging from a vine up in the branches of a tree. The grapes seemed ready to burst with sweet juice. The Fox's mouth watered as he gazed longingly at them.

The bunch hung from a high branch, and the Fox had to jump for it. The first time he jumped he missed it by a long way. So he walked off a short distance and took a running leap at it. He fell short once more. Again and again he tried, but each time, he could not reach the grapes.

Now he sat down and looked up at the grapes in disgust.

"What a fool I am," he said. "Here I am wearing myself out to get a bunch of grapes. They are not worth my effort. I am sure they are sour."

And he walked off with his nose in the air.

*There are many who belittle
what they cannot get.*

The Gnat and the Bull

A small Gnat flew over the meadow with much buzzing. It settled on the tip of one of the horns of a Bull. After he had rested a while, he got ready to fly away, and he buzzed to the Bull:

"I beg your pardon for using your horn for a resting place. I'm sorry to have been such a burden to you. You must be very glad to have me go now."

"Oh?" replied the Bull. "I did not even know you were there."

We are often of greater importance in our own eyes than in the eyes of our neighbor.

The Shepherd Boy and the Wolf

A Shepherd Boy tended his father's Sheep near a dark forest not far from the village. Soon he found life in the pasture very dull. All he could do to amuse himself was talk to his dog or play on his shepherd's pipe.

One day as he sat watching the Sheep, he looked over at the quiet forest. "I wonder if I will ever see a Wolf?" he said to himself. "That would certainly be frightening!" And so he thought of a way to create some excitement.

His father had told him to call for help if a Wolf attacked the flock, and the Villagers would drive it away. So now, though he had not seen anything that even looked like a Wolf, he ran toward the village shouting at the top of his voice:

"Wolf! Wolf!"

As he expected, the Villagers who heard the cry dropped their work and ran in great excitement to the pasture. But when they got there, they found the Boy doubled up with laughter at the trick he had played on them.

A few days later the Shepherd Boy again shouted, "Wolf! Wolf!"

Again the Villagers ran to help him, only to be laughed at again.

Then one evening, as the sun was setting behind the forest and the shadows were creeping out over the pasture, a Wolf really did spring from the forest and fall upon the Sheep.

In terror, the Boy ran toward the village, shouting, "Wolf! Wolf!"

But, even though the Villagers heard the cry, they did not run to help him as they had before.

"He cannot fool us again," they said.

The Wolf killed a great many of the Boy's Sheep and then slipped away into the forest.

Liars are not believed
even when they speak the truth.

The Sheep and the Pig

One day a Shepherd discovered a fat Pig in the same meadow as his Sheep. He very quickly captured the porker, which squealed at the top of its voice the moment the Shepherd laid his hands on it. You would have thought, to hear the loud squeals, that the Pig was being cruelly hurt. Indeed, the Pig did squeal and struggle to escape. But the Shepherd tucked his prize under his arm and started off to the butcher shop in the marketplace.

The Sheep in the meadow were amazed and amused at how the Pig was behaving. They followed the Shepherd with the Pig to the gate at the far end of the meadow.

"What makes you squeal like that?" asked one of the Sheep. "The Shepherd often catches and carries off one of us. But we would be ashamed to make such a terrible fuss about it like you do."

"That is all very well for you," replied the Pig, with a squeal and a frantic kick. "When he catches you, he is only after your wool. When he catches hold of me, he wants my bacon!"

It is easy to be brave when there is no danger.

The Travelers and the Purse

Two men were traveling along the road when one of them picked up a purse filled with coins.

"How lucky I am!" he said. "I found a purse!"

"Do not say '*I* found a purse,' " said his friend. "Say '*we* found a purse.' Friends who travel together should share."

"No, no," replied the other. "I found it and I am going to keep it."

Just then they heard a shout of "Stop, thief!" Looking around, they saw a mob of people with clubs coming down the road.

The man who had found the purse became fearful. "We are lost if they find the purse on us!" he cried.

"No, no," replied the other. "You would not say 'we' before, so now stick to your 'I'. Say '*I* am lost.' "

We cannot expect anyone to share our misfortunes unless we are willing to share our good fortune also.

The Oak and the Reeds

A giant Oak stood near a brook among some slender Reeds. When the wind blew, the great Oak stood proudly upright with its many arms uplifted to the sky. But the Reeds bowed low in the wind and sang a sad and mournful song.

"You have reason to complain," said the Oak. "The slightest breeze that ruffles the water makes you bow your heads. Yet I, the mighty Oak, stand upright and firm before the howling storm."

"Do not worry about us," replied the Reeds. "The winds do not harm us. We bow before them and so we do not break. You, in all your pride and strength, have so far resisted their blows. But the end is coming."

As the Reeds spoke, a great hurricane rushed out of the north. The Oak stood proudly and fought against the storm, while the Reeds bowed low. A great wind blew, and all at once the great tree fell, torn up by the roots, and lay among the Reeds.

Better to bow when it is folly to resist,
than to resist stubbornly and be destroyed.

The Rooster and the Jewel

A Rooster was scratching about to find something to eat for himself and his family. By chance he turned up a jewel that had been lost by its owner.

"Aha!" said the Rooster. "I am sure you are a costly jewel. Whoever lost you would give much to find you. But, as for me, I would choose a single grain of barley before all the jewels in the world."

Lovely things have no value
to those who do not prize them.

The Wolf and the Crane

A Wolf had been eating greedily, and a bone had stuck in his throat. He could not get it to come out or go down, and of course he could not eat a thing. This was an awful situation for the Wolf.

So away he hurried to the Crane. He was sure that she, with her long neck and bill, would easily be able to reach the bone and pull it out.

"I will reward you well," said the Wolf, "if you pull that bone out for me."

The Crane, as you can imagine, was very uneasy about putting her head in a Wolf's throat. But she was kind by nature, so she did what the Wolf asked her to do.

When the Wolf felt that the bone was gone, he started to walk away.

"What about my reward?" called the Crane.

"What!" snarled the Wolf, whirling around. "Haven't you got it? Isn't it enough that I let you take your head out of my mouth without snapping it off?"

Expect no reward for serving the wicked.

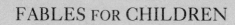

The Plane Tree

Two Travelers, walking in the noonday sun, decided to rest in the shade of a wide-spreading tree. As they lay looking up among the pleasant leaves, they saw that it was a Plane Tree.

"How useless is the Plane Tree!" said one of them. "It gives no fruit, and in the fall, it just litters the ground with leaves."

"Useless?" said the Plane Tree. "There you lie in my cooling shade. You two fools are ungrateful and don't deserve the blessing of my shade."

Our best blessings are often
the least appreciated.

The Vain Jackdaw and His Borrowed Feathers

A Jackdaw flew over the garden of the King's palace. There he saw with much wonder and envy a flock of royal Peacocks with splendid tail-feathers.

Now, the Jackdaw was not a very handsome bird. "Surely all I need to do is to dress like a Peacock in order to become quite a fine-looking fellow," he decided. So he flew down and picked up some colorful feathers off the ground and stuck them among his own black feathers.

Dressed in his borrowed feathers, he strutted among the other jackdaws with his nose in the air. *Oh, how fine I look!* he thought. *Oh, how jealous the other jackdaws must be!*

Then he flew down into the garden among the Peacocks. But they soon saw who he was—a cheat! They flew at him, angrily plucking away the borrowed feathers—and also some of his own black feathers.

The poor Jackdaw returned sadly home. And there another surprise awaited him.

The jackdaws had not forgotten how he had strutted about with his fine feathers. To punish him, they drove him away, pecking at his black tail-feathers.

Borrowed feathers do not make fine birds.

The Frogs Who Wished for a King

The Frogs were tired of having no rules or ruler. They had always been able to do whatever they chose to do. They had so much freedom that it had spoiled them. They did nothing but sit around croaking in a bored manner and wishing for a government that could entertain them. How fun it would be to have a royal king. How grand it would be to have a king rule them in a way to make them know they were being ruled. No weak government for them, they declared. So they sent a request to Jupiter, the king of the gods, asking for a king.

Jupiter saw what simple and foolish creatures they were. To keep them quiet and make them think they had a king, he threw down a huge log, which fell into the water with a great splash. The Frogs hid themselves among the reeds and grasses, thinking the new king to be some fearful giant. But they soon discovered how tame and boring King Log was.

In a short time, the younger Frogs were using him for a diving board, while the older Frogs made him a meeting place, where they complained loudly to Jupiter about the government.

"These silly Frogs think they need a king to rule them," said Jupiter. "They do not think they can rule themselves. How foolish they are! I must teach them a lesson."

And so the ruler of the gods sent a Crane to be king of Frogland. The Crane turned out to be a very different sort of king from old King Log. He gobbled up the poor Frogs right and left, and they soon saw what fools they had been. With sad, pitiful croaks they begged Jupiter to take away the cruel king before they were all eaten.

"Aha!" cried Jupiter. "You are not now happy? You have what you asked for—and so you have only yourselves to blame for your misfortunes."

Before you ask for change,
make sure the change will make your life better.

The Crow and the Pitcher

In a spell of dry weather, when the Birds could find very little to drink, a thirsty Crow found a pitcher with a little water in it. But the pitcher was high and had a narrow neck. No matter how he tried, the Crow could not reach the water. He felt as if he would die of thirst.

Then an idea came to him. Picking up some small pebbles, he dropped them into the pitcher one by one. With each pebble the water rose a little higher. The Crow kept dropping in pebbles until at last the water was near enough to the top so that he could drink.

A good use of wits may help you out.

The Ants and the Grasshopper

One bright day in late autumn, a family of Ants was bustling about in the warm sunshine. They were busy drying out all the grain they had stored up during the summer. Along came a starving Grasshopper with his fiddle under his arm. He came up and humbly begged for a bite to eat.

"What!" cried the Ants in surprise. "Haven't you stored anything away for the winter? What in the world were you doing all last summer?"

"Oh, well, I didn't have time to store up any food," said the Grasshopper. "I was busy making music and having fun. Before I knew it, the summer was gone."

The Ants shrugged their shoulders in disgust.

"Making music, were you?" they cried. "Very well—then, now you can dance!" And they turned their backs on the Grasshopper and went on with their work.

There's a time for work
and a time for play.

The Bear and the Bees

A Bear was walking through the woods in search of berries. He came across a fallen tree in which a swarm of Bees had stored their honey. The Bear began to nose around the log very carefully to find out if the Bees were at home. Just then, one of the Bees came home from the clover field with a load of sweets. The Bee guessed what the Bear was after, and she flew at him, stung him sharply, and then disappeared into the hollow log.

The Bear lost his temper in an instant. He sprang upon the log, tooth and claw, to destroy the nest. But this only brought out the whole swarm. The poor Bear had to take to his heels with the swarm after him. He was able to save himself only by diving into a pool of water.

It is wiser to put up with a single injury in silence than to bring on a thousand by flying into a rage.

The Stag and His Reflection

A Stag was drinking from a clear spring when he saw himself in the water. He greatly admired the graceful arch of his antlers, but he was very much ashamed of his thin legs.

"How can it be," he sighed, "that I have such thin, weak-looking legs when I have such a magnificent crown of antlers?"

At that moment he smelled a Panther. In an instant the Stag was bounding away through the forest. But as he ran, his wide-spreading antlers caught in the branches of the trees, and soon the Panther overtook him. Then the Stag realized that his thin legs would have saved him had it not been for the useless, fancy antlers on his head.

We often value that which is lovely to look at more than what is useful.

The Donkey and the Load of Salt

A Merchant, driving his Donkey homeward from the seashore with a heavy load of salt, came to a stream. They had crossed this stream safely many times before, but this time the Donkey slipped and fell when halfway over. When the Merchant at last got him to his feet, much of the salt had melted away into the water. The Donkey found that his load was much lighter. How delighted he was! And so he finished the journey home very happily.

The next day, the Merchant went for another load of salt. On the way home, the clever Donkey let himself fall into the water, and again got rid of most of the heavy salt.

The angry Merchant turned around and drove the Donkey back to the seashore, where he loaded him with two great baskets of sponges. At the stream, the Donkey again tumbled over. But when he got to his feet, he found that the sponges were filled with water! The Donkey dragged himself home under a load ten times heavier than before.

What works for one situation
will not work for another.

The Rabbits and the Frogs

Rabbits, as you know, are very timid. Even a shadow can send them scurrying to a hiding place. One day, as they were passing a pond, they were saying how ashamed they were to be so timid. A family of Frogs was sitting among the reeds. The Frogs heard the Rabbits and in an instant they jumped into the water.

"Look!" cried a Rabbit. "Things are not so bad. There are creatures who are even afraid of us!"

No matter how low you feel,
there is always someone worse off.

The Bundle of Sticks

A Father had a family of Sons who were always arguing among themselves. No words he could say did any good. He decided to think of a way to show them that bickering would lead to no good end.

One day, when his Sons had been arguing and sulking more than usual, he asked one of them to bring him a bundle of sticks. Then, handing the bundle to each of his Sons in turn, he told them to try to break it. Each one tried his best, but none was able to do so.

The Father then untied the bundle and gave the sticks to his Sons to break one by one. This they did very easily.

"My Sons," said the Father, "do you not see how certain it is that if you agree with each other and help each other, it will be impossible for your enemies to injure you? But if you are divided among yourselves, you will be no stronger than a single stick in that bundle."

In unity is strength.

The Two Stubborn Goats

There were once two Goats who were each walking on opposite rocky sides of a mountain valley. It so happened that a large tree had fallen, forming a bridge between the two sides. Far beneath this bridge there flowed a wild river.

Now, the two Goats each started to cross the bridge and looked up and saw each other. The trunk of the tree was large, but not large enough for one animal to pass another safely. One Goat would have to wait for the other to cross. And do you think one Goat would back up and allow the other to pass? No! These Goats were both too stubborn!

One Goat set his foot on the log. The other did also. Each kept walking until they met in the middle, horn to horn. Neither would back up nor step aside. Instead, they locked horns and pushed at each other—and both fell, down, down, down into the river below.

It is better to step aside
than to stubbornly step into disaster.

The Boys and the Frogs

Some Boys were playing one day at the edge of a pond where a family of Frogs happened to live. The Boys were laughing and making a game of throwing stones into the pond to see if they could skip them across the top of the water.

The stones were flying thick and fast and the Boys were enjoying themselves very much. But the poor Frogs in the pond were trembling with fear.

At last one of the Frogs, the oldest and bravest, put his head out of the water and said, "Oh, please, dear children, stop your cruel play! Though it may be fun for you, it means death to us!"

Always be sure your fun is not the cause of another's unhappiness.

What the Young Mouse Saw

A very young Mouse had never seen anything of the world. When he went out from his home for the first time, he almost came to a sad end. And this is the story he told his mother about his adventures.

"I was strolling along very happily. Just as I turned the corner into the next yard, I saw two strange creatures. One of them had a very kind and sweet look. I did not fear it at all. But the other was the most fearful monster you can think of. You should have seen him!

"On top of his head and in front of his neck there were red pieces of raw meat. He walked about, tearing up the ground with his toes, and beating his arms against his sides. The moment he saw me, he opened his pointed mouth as if to swallow me. Then he let out a loud roar that frightened me almost to death!"

Can you guess who it was that the young Mouse was trying to describe to his mother? It was nobody but the barnyard Rooster. It was the first one the little Mouse had ever seen, so of course, it was quite a sight to him.

"Oh, Mother," said the Mouse. "How I wish that terrible monster had not been there! I wanted so much to meet the pretty creature, who looked so good and gentle. She had thick, soft fur, a sweet face, and such a calm look, though her eyes were bright and shining. As she looked at me she waved her fine long tail and smiled. I am sure she was just about to speak to me when that awful monster I have told you about let out a screaming yell, and I ran for my life."

And can you guess who the pretty creature was that charmed the young Mouse?

"My son," said the Mother Mouse, "that gentle creature you saw was none other than the Cat. She may have a kind-looking face, but she does not like mice! The other was nothing but a bird who wouldn't harm you in the least. As for the Cat, she eats us. So be thankful, my child, that you escaped with your life. Remember, don't trust looks to determine someone's heart."

Do not judge someone's nature by his looks alone.

Hercules and the Farmer

A Farmer was driving his wagon along a soggy country road. The horses could hardly drag the load through the deep mud. At last they came to a standstill when a wheel sank in a rut.

The Farmer climbed down from his seat and stood beside the wagon, looking at it, making no effort to get it out of the rut. All he did was mutter about his bad luck and call loudly on Hercules to come to his aid. Then, it is said, Hercules appeared, saying:

"Put your shoulder to the wheel, man, and urge on your horses. Do you think you can move the wagon by simply whining about it? Hercules will not help unless you make some effort to help yourself."

And when the Farmer put his shoulder to the wheel and urged on the horses, the wagon moved slowly but surely. Soon the Farmer was again riding along with a good lesson learned.

Heaven helps those who help themselves.

The Lion, the Bear, and the Fox

Just as a great Bear rushed upon a stray Goat, a Lion leaped in upon the same prey. The two fought for the prize until each was so wounded that both sank down to rest. Just then a Fox dashed up and made off with the Goat as fast as he could go. The Lion and the Bear looked on in helpless rage.

"It would have been better for us," said the Lion, "if we had agreed to share the meal."

Those who battle for gain may risk loss of all.

The Proud Lion and the Donkey

One day the King of Beasts walked proudly down a path. The animals stepped aside to let him pass and bowed to him. However, one Donkey brayed rudely as the Lion passed.

The Lion felt a flash of anger. But when he saw who had spoken, he walked quietly on. The great Lion would not raise one claw or bother himself with such a fool.

Do not listen to the words of a fool. Ignore them.

The Wolf and His Shadow

A Wolf left his den one evening feeling fit and strong, but hungry. As he ran, the setting sun cast his shadow far out on the ground. The long shadow made the Wolf seem a hundred times bigger than he really was.

"How grand!" exclaimed the Wolf proudly. "See how big I am! I'm bigger than a Lion! Why, if I see one of those little beasts, I have no need to fear at all. Imagine me running away from a little Lion! I'll show *him* who is fit to be king, he or I."

Just then, an even larger shadow was cast next to the Wolf's shadow. The next instant, a Lion struck him down with a single blow.

Do not let your imagination
make you forget reality.

The Wolf and the Lamb

A Wolf was lapping at a spring on a hillside. He looked up and saw a little Lamb just beginning to drink downstream.

There's supper, he thought, *if only I can find some excuse to seize it.* So the Wolf went down and called out to the Lamb, "How dare you muddy up my water!"

"But, sir," replied the meek Lamb, "you were upstream and I am downstream. I cannot muddy the water you drink up there."

"Well, then," said the Wolf, "why did you call me bad names this time last year?"

"That cannot be," said the Lamb. "I am only six months old."

"If it wasn't you, it was your brother!"

"I have no brothers."

"I don't care!" growled the Wolf. "If not a brother, then it was your father!"

And with that, he rushed upon the poor Lamb and carried her off.

Any excuse will do for a bully.

The Wolf and the Lion

A Wolf had stolen a Lamb and was carrying it off to his den to eat it. But his plans were changed when he met a Lion. The Lion, without so much as a word or excuse, growled and took the Lamb away from him.

The Wolf trotted off to a safe distance. Then he called in a stern tone:

"You have no right to take my meal like that!"

The Lion looked back angrily. But because the Wolf was too far away to be taught a lesson with a swift swipe of his paw, the Lion said:

"Your meal? Did you buy it, or did the Shepherd give it to you? Please tell me, how did *you* get it?"

What is ill-won can be ill-lost.

The Wolf at the Shepherd's Hut

A Wolf looked into a hut and saw the Shepherd and his family feasting on a roasted lamb.

"Ha!" he muttered. "If the Shepherd had caught *me* feasting on a lamb, what a great shouting and running about there would have been! I would be hunted down and punished!"

Men often see no wrong in doing
that which they don't allow others to do.

The Lion and the Mosquito

"Away with you, vile insect!" said a Lion angrily to a Mosquito that was buzzing around his head. But the Mosquito paid no attention to the great beast.

"Do you think," he said to the Lion with a sneer, "that I am afraid of you because they call you King?"

The next instant he flew at the Lion and stung him sharply on the nose. Mad with rage, the Lion struck fiercely at the Mosquito, but only succeeded in tearing himself with his claws. Again and again the Mosquito stung the Lion, who now was roaring terribly. At last, worn out with rage and covered with wounds that his own teeth and claws had made, the Lion gave up the fight.

The Mosquito buzzed away to tell the whole world about his victory, but instead he flew straight into a spider's web. And there, he who had defeated the King of Beasts came to a sad end, the prey of a little spider.

Don't let pride blind you to pitfalls.

The Peacock's Tail

The Peacock, they say, did not at first have the beautiful feathers he now has. It seems that there was a time when the Peacock begged Juno, the queen of the gods, for a rich train of feathers grander than any other bird. Juno granted his request. With his new gleaming tail of green, gold, purple, and blue, he strutted around proudly among the other birds. All who saw him envied him, which pleased the vain Peacock greatly.

The Peacock then saw an Eagle soaring high up in the blue sky. "Ah!" said the Peacock. "How amazing I will look when I fly with my new robe of feathers."

Lifting his wings, the Peacock tried to rise from the ground. But the weight of his magnificent train held him down. Never again could he fly up to greet the first rays of the morning sun or the rosy clouds at sunset. Instead he would have to walk the ground with his long, heavy tail of beautiful, royal feathers.

Gain of riches can also bring loss of freedom.

The Heron

A Heron was walking along the bank of a stream. He kept his eyes on the clear water, with his long neck and pointed bill ready to snap up something tasty for his breakfast. The clear water was filled with fish, but the Heron was hard to please that morning.

"No little fish for me," he said with a sniff when he spotted some Minnows. "So small a meal is not fit for a Heron."

Now a fine young Perch swam near.

"No, indeed," said the Heron. "I wouldn't even trouble to open my beak for anything that small!"

As the sun rose, the fish left the shallow water near the shore and swam below to the cooler waters in the middle of the stream. The Heron saw no more fish. Weary and hungry, he was glad at last to breakfast on a tiny Snail.

If you are too hard to please,
you may end up with hardly anything.

The Young Fox
and the Lion

A very young Fox had never before seen a Lion. When he met one in the forest, he took off at top speed for a hiding place.

The second time the Fox saw the Lion, he hid behind a tree a moment before sneaking away. But the third time, the Fox went boldly up to the Lion and said, "Hello, there, old friend."

It's too easy to feel safe with something familiar.

The Wolf and the Clever Donkey

A Donkey was feeding in a field near a wood. He chanced to see a Wolf sneaking along in the shadows behind some bushes. He easily guessed what the Wolf had in mind. *I must have a plan to save myself*, he thought. So he pretended he had been hurt in the foot and began to walk about as if he were in great pain.

When the Wolf came up, he asked the Donkey how he had hurt his foot.

"I have stepped on a sharp thorn," replied the Donkey. "Oh, it hurts!"

"How I wish I could help you, my friend," said the Wolf, "but, you see, I would rather make you into my next meal."

"Oh, but you are so skilled. Please pull it out," groaned the Donkey. "If you do not, it might stick in your throat when you eat me."

The Wolf saw the wisdom of the advice. For, indeed, he wanted to enjoy his meal without any danger of choking. So the Donkey lifted up his foot, and the Wolf began to search very closely and carefully for the thorn.

Just then the Donkey kicked out with all his might, hitting the Wolf right on the nose. The Wolf went tumbling head over heels. And while the Wolf was getting very slowly and painfully to his feet, the Donkey ran away in safety.

"Serves me right," growled the Wolf as he crept into the bushes. "I'm a hunter, not a doctor."

Stick to what you do best.

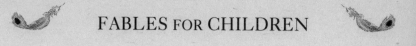

The Fox and the Goat

A Fox, watching a hawk in the sky, fell right into a well. It was not very deep, yet he found that he could not get out again.

After the Fox had been in the well a long time, a thirsty Goat came by. The silly Goat thought the Fox had gone down the well to drink. "Is the water good?" he asked.

"The finest in the whole country," said the crafty Fox. "Jump in and try it. There is more than enough for both of us."

The Goat quickly jumped in and began to drink. The Fox just as quickly jumped onto the Goat's back and leaped from the tip of the Goat's horns out of the well.

The foolish Goat now saw the situation he had gotten into. He begged the Fox to help him out. But the Fox was already on his way to the woods.

"If you had had more sense, ol' fellow," he said as he ran, "you would have thought of finding a way out again before you so eagerly jumped in."

Never leap into the unknown
without an escape plan.

The Farmer and His Sons

A rich old Farmer, who felt that he had not many more days to live, called his Sons to his bedside.

"My Sons," he said, "listen to what I have to say to you. Do not sell the land that has been in our family for many years. Somewhere on it is hidden a rich treasure. I do not know the exact spot, but it is there, and you will surely find it if you search hard for it. Dig and leave no spot unturned."

The Father died. The Sons set to work digging with all their might, turning up every foot of ground with their spades. They went over the whole farm two or three times.

They found no hidden gold. However, their well-turned farmland produced their best harvest ever. They sold more wheat and vegetables than their neighbors. Then they understood that the treasure their father had told them about was the wealth of a bountiful crop that came from the land. Through their hard work and digging they had discovered gold indeed.

Hard work produces a treasure.

The Astrologer

A man who lived a long time ago believed that he could read the future in the stars. He called himself an Astrologer, and spent his time at night gazing up into the sky.

One evening he was walking along the open road outside the village. His eyes were fixed on the stars. He thought he saw there that the end of the world was near. All at once, down he went into a hole full of mud and water.

There he stood up to his ears in the muddy water. He clawed at the slippery sides of the hole but could not climb out.

The frightened Astrologer cried for help. Soon some villagers came running. As they pulled him out of the mud, one of them said:

"You pretend to read the future in the stars, and yet you fail to see what is at your feet! This may teach you to pay more attention to what is right in front of you, and let the future take care of itself."

It is of no use to read the stars
if you can't see what's right here on the earth.

The Dog in the Manger

A Dog was asleep in a manger filled with hay. He was awakened by the Cows, who came in tired and hungry from working in the field. The Dog leaped up and would not let the Cows get near the manger. He snarled and snapped at them as if to say, "This is mine!"

The Cattle looked at the Dog in disgust. "How selfish he is!" said one. "*He* cannot eat the hay, and yet he will not let *us* eat it."

When the farmer came and saw how the Dog was acting, he took a stick and drove him out.

Why keep and deny to others
what you cannot enjoy yourself?

The Wolf and the House Dog

There was once a Wolf who got very little to eat because the Dogs of the village were so wide awake and watchful. He was nothing but skin and bones, and it made him downhearted to think of it.

One night this Wolf happened to meet a fine, fat House Dog who had wandered a little too far from home. *He looks like he'd make a fine meal*, thought the hungry Wolf, *but he also looks strong enough to leave his marks on me.* So the Wolf decided to speak humbly to the Dog. "How fine and fit you look, dear sir," said the Wolf.

"Why, thank you," replied the Dog. "You can be as well-fed as I am if you want to. Just leave the woods. It's a sad life in the woods. Why, you have to fight hard for every bite you get. Follow my example and you will get along quite well."

"What must I do?" asked the Wolf.

"Hardly anything," answered the House Dog. "Chase people in carriages. Bark at strangers. Show happiness at seeing the people of the house. If you do all this you will get tidbits of every kind—chicken bones, bits of meat—as well as kind words and gentle pats."

Oh, how wonderful this sounded to the Wolf! He began to see himself with a new life. But just then he saw that the hair on the Dog's neck was worn and the skin was pink and raw.

"What is that on your neck?"

"Nothing at all," replied the Dog.

"What? Nothing?"

"Well, I guess you see the mark of my collar which is attached to a chain."

"What? A chain?" cried the Wolf. "Don't you go wherever you please?"

"Not always. But what does that matter?"

"A great deal! It is all the difference in the world! I don't care a bit for your fine life, if it means I'd be a captive. I would rather hunt and be hungry than be chained in a yard."

And away ran the Wolf to the woods.

There is nothing worth so much as freedom.

The Eagle and the Jackdaw

A powerful Eagle swooped down, grabbed a Lamb in her claws, and flew off with it to her nest. A silly Jackdaw saw this and thought, "I could do that!" So he flew onto the back of a large Ram and tried to fly off with it. But he was too small and his claws were tangled in the wool.

The Shepherd saw the fluttering Jackdaw. He freed the bird and clipped its wings. That evening he gave the Jackdaw to his children as a play pet.

Know your strengths and your limits.

The Dog and the Oyster

There was a Dog who liked to eat eggs. He was so greedy, he gobbled them whole. One day the Dog strolled down to the seashore. There he saw an Oyster. Quick as a wink, the Dog ate the oyster, shell and all. Oh, how it pained him!

"I've learned that all round things are not eggs," he said, groaning.

Act quickly, regret quickly—and often in pain.

The Helpful Wolf

A Wolf had been prowling around a flock of Sheep for a long time. The Shepherd watched very closely to prevent the Wolf from carrying off a lamb. But the Wolf did not try to do any harm. Instead he seemed to be helping the Shepherd watch and take care of the Sheep. At last the Shepherd got so used to seeing the Wolf around that he forgot how wicked he could be.

One day the Shepherd even went so far as to leave his flock in the Wolf's care while he went to market. But when he came back he saw that many of his Sheep had been killed and carried off. He knew then how foolish he had been to trust a Wolf.

Once a wolf, always a wolf.

The Oxen and the Wheels

A pair of Oxen was pulling a loaded wagon along a muddy road. They used all their strength to pull the heavy load, but they did not complain.

The Wheels of the wagon had an easier job. All they had to do was turn. However, they fussed and creaked and groaned at every turn. The poor Oxen, pulling the wagon through the deep mud, had their ears filled with the loud whining of the Wheels. And this made their work much harder.

"Silence!" the Oxen cried at last. "Why are you Wheels complaining so loudly? We are pulling all the weight, not you, yet we keep still about it."

Those who suffer least often complain the most.

The Wise Rooster and the Fox

One evening, as the sun was sinking, a wise old Rooster flew into a tree to roost. Before he settled himself for rest, he flapped his wings three times and crowed loudly. But just as he was about to put his head under his wing, his sharp eyes caught a flash of red and the sight of a long pointed nose. There—just below him—stood the Fox.

"Have you heard the wonderful news?" cried the Fox cheerfully.

"What news?" asked the Rooster calmly. But he had a fluttery feeling inside him, for, you know, he was very much afraid of the Fox.

"Your family and mine and all other animals have agreed to live in peace and friendship from now on, forever. Just think of it! I simply cannot wait to give you a hug! Do come down, dear friend, and let us celebrate the joyful event."

"How grand!" said the Rooster. "I certainly am delighted at the news."

But as the Rooster spoke these words, he stretched up on his tiptoes. He seemed to be looking at something far off in the distance.

"What is it you see, dear friend?" asked the Fox a little nervously.

"Why, it looks to me like a couple of Dogs coming this way. They must have heard the good news and—"

But the Fox did not wait to hear more. Off he started on a run.

"Wait!" cried the Rooster. "Why do you run? Surely all these Dogs are friends of yours now!"

"Yes," answered the Fox, "but they might not have heard the news. Besides, I have an important chore to do that I almost forgot about."

The Rooster smiled as he buried his head in his feathers and went to sleep, for he had outwitted a very crafty enemy.

The trickster is easily tricked.

Mercury and the Woodman

A poor Woodman was cutting wood near the edge of a deep pool in the forest. The Woodman was tired, for he had been working since sunrise. Thus it happened that the axe slipped and flew out of his hands into the pool. The Woodman was in despair. This was his only axe and he had no money for a new one. And so he wept beside the pool.

Suddenly, the god Mercury appeared!

"What is your trouble?" asked the god.

The Woodman told him what had happened. Right away, the kind Mercury dived into the pool. When he came up again he held a wonderful axe made of gold.

"Is this your axe?" Mercury asked.

The axe of gold was worth a lot of money! But the honest Woodman said, "No, that is not my axe."

Mercury put the golden axe on the bank and sprang back into the pool. This time he brought up an axe of silver. But the poor Woodman told Mercury that his axe was just a plain one with a wooden handle.

Mercury dived down for the third time. When he came up, he had the very axe that had been lost.

The Woodman was very glad that his axe had been found. "I cannot thank you enough!" he said.

"I admire your honesty," Mercury said. "As a reward you may have all three axes—the gold and the silver as well as your own."

The happy Woodman returned to his home with his treasures. Soon the story of his good fortune was known to everybody in the village.

Now, there were several men in the village who believed that they could easily win the same good fortune. They hurried out into the woods, one here, one there. They hid their axes in the bushes. Then they wept and called on Mercury to help them find their lost axes.

And indeed Mercury did appear, first to this one, then to that. To each one he showed an axe of gold. Each one eagerly said, "Oh, yes, that is my axe!" But Mercury did not give them the golden axe. Oh, no! Instead he gave them each a hard whack over the head with it and sent them home.

And when the dishonest men returned the next day to look for their own axes, they were nowhere to be found.

The honest man is rewarded.

The Two Travelers and the Bear

Two Men were traveling together through a forest. All at once, a huge Bear crashed out of the brush near them. One of the Men, thinking of his own safety, climbed a tree. The other, unable to fight the huge beast alone, threw himself onto the ground and lay still, as if he were dead. He had heard that a Bear will not touch a dead body.

It must have been true, for the Bear bent its head down and sniffed the Man's head awhile. The Bear seemed to think the Man was dead, for then it walked away.

The Man in the tree climbed down.

"It looked just as if that Bear whispered in your ear," he said. "What did he tell you?"

"He said," answered the other, "that it was not at all wise to keep company with a fellow who would leave his friend in a moment of danger."

Misfortune is the test of true friendship.

The Wolf in Sheep's Clothing

A certain Wolf could not get enough to eat because the Shepherds were so watchful. But one night he found a sheep skin that had been cast aside and forgotten. The next day, dressed in the skin, the Wolf strolled into the pasture with the Sheep. Soon a little Lamb was following him about and was quickly led away to become dinner for the Wolf.

That evening the Wolf again joined the flock. But it happened that the Shepherd had decided to make a meal of Sheep, himself. He picked up a knife and went out to the flock.

"Ah, here is a good, plump Sheep," said the Shepherd.

He put his knife to work and killed the Sheep. Imagine his surprise when he discovered a Wolf beneath the sheep skin!

He who does evil to others
often becomes the victim himself.

The Bored Crab

A Crab one day grew bored with his sandy home on the beach. He decided to take a stroll to a grassy meadow beyond the sand dunes. "I'm sure I will find something better there than salty water and sand flies." So off he crawled to the meadow. But a hungry Fox spied him and quickly ate him up, shell, claw, and all.

Sometimes it's best to stay where you best fit.

The Milkmaid and Her Pail

A Milkmaid had been out to milk the cows and was returning from the field. She walked home holding her milk pail balanced upon her head. As she strolled along, her pretty head was busy with plans for the days to come.

"This good, rich milk," she said, "will give me plenty of cream to churn. The butter I make I will take to market, and with the money I get for it I will buy a lot of eggs for hatching. How nice it will be when they are all hatched and the yard is full of fine young chicks. Then when May Day comes, I will sell them, and with the money I'll buy a lovely new dress to wear to the fair. All the young men will look at me. They will try to talk with me—but I shall toss my head and look away!"

And so saying, she tossed her head—and down fell the pail of milk to the ground! All the milk flowed out, and with it went her dreams of butter and eggs and chicks and a pretty, new dress.

Don't count your chickens before they're hatched.

The Frog and the Mouse

A sly, cruel Frog saw a young Mouse running along the bank of his pond. He swam to the bank and croaked, "Won't you come in and visit with me? I can promise you a good time if you do."

"Oh, sir, I'd love to see another part of the world," said the young Mouse, "but I don't dare go into the pond without your help."

So the crafty Frog tied the Mouse's leg to his own with a reed. Then into the pond he jumped, dragging the foolish Mouse with him.

The Mouse soon had enough of it and wanted to return to shore. But the cruel Frog pulled the Mouse down under the water and drowned him.

Before the Frog could untie the reed, a Hawk came sailing over the pond. Seeing the body of the Mouse floating on the water, the Hawk swooped down, seized the Mouse and carried it off, with the Frog dangling from its leg. Thus at one swoop, the Hawk had caught both meat and fish for his dinner.

Those who seek to harm others
often come to harm themselves.

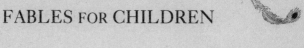

The Ant and the Dove

A Dove saw an Ant fall into a stream. The poor Ant struggled to move through the water to reach the bank, but all his attempts failed. The Dove felt sorry for the Ant, and she dropped a blade of tall grass close beside it. The Ant was able to grab onto and cling to the blade of grass, and he floated safely to shore.

Soon after, the Ant saw a man getting ready to kill the Dove with a stone. But just as the man cast the stone, the Ant stung him on the heel. The pain caused the man to miss his aim, and the Dove flew to safety in a distant forest.

A kindness is never wasted.

The Goose and the Golden Eggs

There was once a Man who had the most wonderful Goose you can imagine. Every day when the Man visited the nest, the Goose had laid a beautiful, glittering, golden egg.

The Man took the golden eggs to market and soon began to get rich. He happily bought fine foods and fine clothes with his money.

Before long, the Man wanted to own a fine house, too. But the Goose only gave him a single golden egg a day. He was not getting rich fast enough to buy a large house.

Then one day, after he had finished counting his money, an idea came to him. "I could get all the golden eggs at once if I kill the Goose and cut it open!" he said.

But when the deed was done, not a single golden egg did he find. His precious Goose was dead—and could make no more golden eggs.

Those who have plenty often want more,
and may end up losing all they have.

The North Wind and the Sun

The North Wind and the Sun had a quarrel about which of them was the stronger. The North Wind insisted that he had greater strength, for he could move ships on the sea. The Sun insisted that he had greater strength, for he could bring forth life from the land.

While they were arguing, a Traveler passed along the road wrapped in a cloak.

The Sun nodded toward the man. "Let us agree," said the Sun, "that he is the stronger who can strip that Traveler of his cloak."

"Very well," growled the North Wind.

At once, the Wind sent a cold, howling blast against the Traveler.

With the first gust of wind, the ends of the cloak whipped about the Traveler's body. The North Wind was pleased. But the cloak did not blow off, for the Traveler wrapped it closely around him. The harder the Wind blew, the tighter the Traveler held onto the cloak. The North Wind tore angrily at the cloak with all his strength, but he could not pull it from the man.

Then the Sun began to shine. At first his beams were gentle. The weather became pleasant and warm after the bitter cold of the Wind. The Traveler unfastened his cloak and let it hang loosely from his shoulders. The Sun's rays grew warmer and warmer. The Traveler took off his cap and wiped his forehead. At last he became so warm from the hot Sun that he pulled off his cloak. To escape the blazing sunshine, he threw himself down in the shade of a tree by the roadside.

The Sun turned to the North Wind and said:

*True strength lies not in force
but in gentle persuasion.*

The Old Lion and the Fox

It was difficult for a certain old Lion to get food. His teeth and claws were not as sharp as they had been in his younger days. And so the Lion pretended to be very sick. He let all his neighbors know about it, and then lay down in his cave to wait for visitors. And when they came to offer him their help, he ate them up one by one.

The Fox came too, but he was more careful than the others. He stood just outside the cave and asked the Lion kindly, "How are you feeling, old fellow?"

The Lion moaned and said he was very ill indeed. He asked the Fox to step into the cave so that he could hear him better. But the Fox very wisely stayed outside.

"I would be glad to do as you ask," said the Fox, "but I see there are many footprints leading into your cave and none coming out. Please tell me, how do your visitors find their way out again?"

Beware the new tricks of an old enemy.

The Donkey and the Lap Dog

There was once a Donkey whose Master also owned a Lap Dog. Now, the Master gave this Lap Dog much attention. He patted its head, spoke sweetly to it, and fed it scraps from the table. Every day the Dog would run to meet the good Master, dancing playfully about and leaping up to lick his hands and face.

The Donkey saw all this and was jealous. He was well fed, to be sure, but he also had much work to do. And the Master hardly ever patted him or spoke kindly to him.

Now, the jealous Donkey got an idea in his silly head. All he had to do to win his Master's favor was to act like the Dog. So one day he left his stable and clattered eagerly into the house.

He found his Master seated at the dinner table. With a loud bray, the Donkey kicked up his heels and pranced around the table, knocking it over! Then he put his front feet on his Master's knees and rolled out his tongue to lick the Master's face, as he had seen the Dog do. But his weight upset the chair, and the Donkey and man rolled over together in the pile of broken dishes from the table.

The Master was much alarmed! Why was his Donkey acting like this? He called for help, and soon his servants came running. When they saw the danger the Master was in, they grabbed at the silly Donkey and beat him and kicked him out the door and all the way back to the stable. There they left him to think about how foolish he had been to try to be something other than a Donkey.

What is welcome and agreeable from one, may be rude and unwanted from another.

The Fox without a Tail

A Fox walking through farmland was caught in a trap by the tail. He tugged and tugged, and after many painful tries, he finally got himself loose. However, he had to leave his beautiful bushy tail behind him.

For a long time he kept away from the other Foxes, for he knew that they would all make fun of him and crack jokes and laugh behind his back. But it was hard for him to live alone, and at last he thought of a plan that would perhaps help him out of his trouble.

He called a meeting of all the Foxes. He told them that he had something of great importance to discuss with the tribe.

When they were all gathered together, the Fox without a tail got up and made a long speech about those Foxes who had come to harm because of their tails.

"One Fox was caught by hunting dogs when his tail became tangled up in a bush," he said. "And another Fox could not run swiftly because of the weight of his tail, so he became a meal for a wolf. Besides, it is well known that men hunt

Foxes simply for their tails, which they cut off as prizes of the hunt. So you see, my friends, tails are quite useless to us, and can be a danger besides."

Then the Fox without a tail stood there with his nose in the air as if he were very smart. "I suggest," he said, "that we all—cut off our tails."

When he had finished talking, an old Fox arose and said, smiling:

"Brother Fox, kindly turn around for a moment, and you will know our answer on this."

When the poor Fox without a tail turned around, the other Foxes pointed and laughed at his stubby tail.

"Just because you have lost your tail," said the old Fox, "does not mean we should lose ours."

Do not listen to the advice of him who seeks to lower you to his own level.

The Lion's Share

A long time ago, the Lion, the Fox, the Jackal, and the Wolf agreed to go hunting together, sharing with each other whatever they found.

One day the Wolf ran down a Stag and called his comrades to divide the meal.

Without being asked, the Lion placed himself at the head of the feast to do the carving. With a great show of fairness, he began to count the guests.

"One," he said, counting on his claws, "that is myself, the Lion. Two, that's the Wolf. Three is the Jackal. And the Fox makes four."

He then very carefully divided the Stag into four equal parts.

"I am King Lion," he said, when he had finished, "so of course I get the first part. This next part falls to me because I am the strongest. And this is mine because I am the bravest."

He now began to glare at the others. "If any of you have any claim to the part that is left," he growled, stretching his claws, "now is the time to speak up."

Might makes right.

The Tortoise and the Hare

A Hare was making fun of the Tortoise one day for being so slow. "Do you ever get anywhere?" he asked with a laugh.

"Yes," said the Tortoise, "and I get there sooner than you think. I'll run you a race and prove it."

The Hare was amused at the idea of running a race with the Tortoise. He agreed to it just for the fun of it. A Fox was asked to be the judge, and he marked the distance and started the runners off.

The Hare was soon far out of sight. To make the Tortoise feel even more foolish for trying to race a Hare, he lay down to take a nap until the Tortoise had caught up.

The Tortoise meanwhile kept going slowly but steadily. After a time he passed the Hare, sleeping peacefully beside the road. When at last the Hare woke up, the Tortoise was near the goal. The Hare now ran his swiftest, but he could not pass the Tortoise in time.

Slow and steady wins the race.

The Miser's Gold

A Miser had buried his gold in a secret place in his garden. Every day he went to the spot. He dug up the treasure and counted it piece by piece to make sure it was all there. He did not know that a Thief was watching him. The Miser made so many trips that the Thief guessed what was hidden. One night, the Thief quietly dug up the treasure and ran off with it.

The Miser went out the next day and discovered that his gold was missing. He was greatly upset. He groaned and cried and held his head in his hands.

A stranger passing by heard his cries and asked what had happened.

"My gold! Oh, my gold!" cried the Miser wildly. "Someone has robbed me!"

"Your gold! Was it there in that hole? Why did you put it there? Why didn't you keep it in the house where you could easily get it when you had to buy things?"

"Buy?" said the Miser angrily. "Why, I never removed my gold. I would not dream of spending any of it—for then I would have less gold!"

The stranger picked up some stones and threw them into the hole.

"If that is the case," he said, "cover up these stones and pretend they are your gold. They will be worth just as much to you as the treasure you lost!"

Riches not put to use have no value.

The Serpent and the Eagle

A Serpent surprised an Eagle and wrapped herself around the Eagle's neck. The Eagle tried to reach the Serpent with his beak and claws, but he could not. The Eagle flew far into the sky, trying to shake off his enemy. But the Serpent's grip grew tighter. Slowly the Eagle sank back to earth, gasping for breath.

A Traveler happened to see this. He felt sorry for the noble Eagle. He rushed up and loosened the Serpent and freed the Eagle.

The Serpent was angry. She had no chance to bite the Traveler. Instead she struck at the water bag attached to the Traveler's belt. Her fangs sank into the bag and let loose her poison.

The Traveler went on toward home. He became thirsty on the way. He stopped at a spring and filled his water bag. Just as he was about to drink, there was a sudden rush of great wings. Sweeping down, the Eagle grabbed the poisoned water bag from out of the man's hands. He flew away with it to hide it where it could never be found.

An act of kindness is well repaid.

The Cat and the Fox

Once a Cat and a Fox were traveling together. As they went along they took turns finding meals—a stray mouse here, a fat chicken there.

"You think you are clever, don't you?" said the Fox after the Cat had caught a mole. "Why, I know a whole sackful of tricks!"

"Well," replied the Cat, "I admit I know only one good trick. But my one trick, let me tell you, is worth a thousand of yours!"

Just then, close by, they heard a hunter's horn and the yelping of a pack of dogs. In an instant the Cat was up a tree, hiding among the leaves.

"This is my trick," he called to the Fox. "Now let me see what is in your sackful of tricks!"

But the Fox had so many plans for escape he could not decide which one to try first. He dodged here and there with the dogs at his heels. He ran at top speed, he entered a dozen burrows. But in the end the dogs caught him, and soon put an end to the Fox with many tricks.

One good skill may be all you need to succeed.

The Rabbit, the Weasel, and the Cat

A Rabbit left his home one day for a dinner of clover. But he forgot to latch the door of his house. While he was gone, a Weasel walked in and calmly made himself at home. When the Rabbit returned, there was the Weasel's nose sticking out of the Rabbit's own doorway.

The Rabbit was quite angry—for a Rabbit— and asked the Weasel to move out. But the Weasel was perfectly happy to stay in the house.

A wise old Cat heard the Rabbit and the Weasel. She offered to settle the matter for them.

"Come close to me," said the Cat, "for I have poor hearing. Put your mouths close to my ears while you tell me the facts."

The Rabbit and the Weasel did as they were told. In an instant the Cat had them both under her claws. And the matter was certainly settled.

It is often best to settle your own matters.

The Dog and His Reflection

A Dog with a bone was crossing a small bridge. He looked down and saw himself reflected in the quiet water. But the Dog thought he saw a real Dog carrying a bone much bigger than his own.

Oh, how the Dog wanted the bigger bone! He snarled and barked—and his bone dropped from his mouth and fell with a splash into the water. The Dog saw the ripples and realized there was no other Dog—and now there was no bone at all.

It is very foolish to be greedy.

The Eagle and the Beetle

An Eagle was chasing a Rabbit who ran to a Beetle for help. The Beetle begged the Eagle to spare the Rabbit. But the Eagle pounced upon her prey. Her great wings slapped the Beetle and sent him tumbling. The furious Beetle flew to the Eagle's nest and rolled out all her eggs. The Eagle did not know who had done this cruel deed, and she cried out with sadness and anger.

The next year, the Eagle built her nest far up on a mountain. But the Beetle found it and again rolled out the eggs. The Eagle went to Jupiter, the king of the gods, and begged, "Let me place my eggs in your lap, where no one will harm them." But the Beetle buzzed around Jupiter's head and told him why he was punishing the Eagle. Jupiter stood up—and the eggs rolled from his lap. "The Eagle's punishment is complete," he said.

And ever after, while the Eagle's eggs lie in the nest in spring, the Beetle still sleeps in the ground. For so Jupiter commanded.

Even the weakest can find a way to right a wrong.

The Fox and the Crow

One bright morning a hungry Fox was following his sharp nose through the forest in search of a bite to eat. He looked up and saw a Crow on a branch of a tree overhead. This was by no means the first Crow the Fox had ever seen. What was different about this Crow was that the lucky Crow held a bit of cheese in her beak.

"No need to search any farther," thought the sly Fox. "Here is a tasty bite for my breakfast."

Up he trotted to the foot of the tree. He looked and smiled, saying. "Good morning to you, beautiful lady!"

The Crow cocked her head to one side and watched the Fox. She did not trust Foxes, so she kept her beak tightly closed on the cheese and did not say good morning.

"What a charming creature you are!" said the Fox. "How your feathers shine! What splendid wings! I'm sure you have a lovely voice, since everything else about you is so perfect. If you would just sing one song, everyone in the forest would call you the Queen of Birds."

The Crow listened to these words and was quite flattered. She forgot all about not trusting a Fox. She forgot about her breakfast. She forgot that she was, after all, a Crow who did not have a lovely voice. All she thought of was how she wanted to be called the Queen of Birds.

So she opened her beak wide to sing. But, of course, instead of a lovely song, out came a loud caw—and down fell the cheese, straight into the Fox's open mouth.

"Thank you," said the Fox sweetly, as he walked off. "I did not enjoy your song, but I will enjoy your cheese."

Beware the one who flatters—
he wants more than your smiles.

The Farmer and the Stork

There was a simple and trusting Stork who was friends with some rather wild Cranes. The Cranes asked the Stork to go with them to a field that had been newly planted with seeds. But this all ended badly with all the birds caught in the Farmer's nets.

The Stork begged the Farmer not to punish him for eating his seeds. "Please let me go," he pleaded. "I belong to the Stork family. You must know that we are honest birds of good character. Besides, I did not know the Cranes were going to steal."

"You may be a very good bird," answered the Farmer, "but I caught you with these thieves, the Cranes, so you will have to share the same punishment with them."

You are judged by the company you keep.

The Mother Goat and Her Kid

Mother Goat was going to market one morning to buy food for herself and her one little Kid.

"Take good care of the house, my son," she said as she carefully latched the door. "Do not let anyone in unless he gives you this password: Trust no Wolf!"

It happened that a Wolf was watching nearby and heard what the Goat had said. So, as soon as Mother Goat was out of sight, up he trotted to the door and knocked.

"Trust no Wolf," said the Wolf softly.

It was the right password, but when the Kid peeped through a crack in the door and saw the gray figure outside, he did not feel at all easy.

"Show me a white hoof," he said, "or I won't let you in."

A white hoof, of course, is not something a Wolf can show. So the Wolf had to go away as hungry as he had come.

"You can never be too sure," said the Kid, when he saw the Wolf trotting off to the woods.

Check twice before deciding once.

The Donkey in the Lion's Skin

A Donkey found a Lion's skin left in the forest by a hunter. He dressed himself in it and had fun rushing out and scaring any animal that passed by. The frightened animals ran off the moment they saw him.

The Donkey enjoyed seeing the animals running away from him, just as if he were King Lion himself! He could not keep himself from laughing with a loud *hee-haw-hee-haw*.

Now, one of the animals that had run away was a Fox. When the Fox heard the *hee-haw*, he stopped running. He trotted back to the Donkey, walked right up to him, and said:

"If you had kept your mouth shut, you might have frightened me, too. But you gave yourself away with that silly bray."

A fool may trick you by how he is dressed,
but his words will soon show what he really is.

The Bees and the Wasps

A rich comb of honey was found in a hollow tree. The Wasps said it belonged to them. The Bees said the treasure was theirs. The Wasps and the Bees began to argue, and their words became angry. It looked like there might be a battle.

At last they agreed to let a judgè decide the matter. So they brought the case before the Hornet, Justice of the Peace in that part of the woods.

The Judge sat before them and listened to the witnesses. Some Ants said they had seen winged creatures near the hollow tree. "The creatures hummed loudly," they said.

"Like us!" cried the Bees.

"Like us!" cried the Wasps.

"And their bodies were striped yellow and black, like Bees," said an Ant.

"But we also look like that!" said the Wasps.

This did not help Judge Hornet decide. "It seems that the honey could belong to the Bees or the Wasps," he said.

Then a wise old Bee spoke up to the Judge.

"Your Honor," he said, "ask both the Bees and the Wasps to build a honeycomb."

The Wasps became quite angry. "That's unfair!" they cried.

Judge Hornet quickly understood why the Wasps were upset. They knew they could not build a honeycomb and fill it with honey.

"It is clear," said the Judge, "who made the comb and who could not have made it. The honey belongs to the Bees."

Ability proves itself by deeds.

The Lark and Her Young Ones

A Lark made her nest in a field of young wheat. As the days passed, the wheat grew tall and her chicks hatched and grew strong.

Then one day, when the ripe golden grain waved in the breeze, the Farmer and his son came into the field.

"This wheat is now ready to cut," said the Farmer. "We must call in our neighbors and friends to help us harvest it."

The young Larks in their nest close by were frightened. They knew they would be in great danger if they did not leave the nest before the cutters came. When the Mother Lark returned with food for them, they told her what they had heard.

"Do not fear, children," said the Mother Lark. "If the Farmer said he would call in his neighbors and friends to help him do his work, this wheat will not be cut for a while yet."

A few days later, the wheat was so ripe, that the grains began to fall to the ground whenever the wind blew.

"If this wheat is not harvested at once," said the Farmer, "we will lose half the crop. We cannot wait any longer for help from our friends. Tomorrow we must begin the work ourselves."

When the young Larks told their mother what they had heard that day, she said:

"Then we must be off at once. When a man decides to do his own work, and not depend on anyone else, then there will be no more delay."

There was much fluttering as the young Larks tried their small wings that afternoon. At sunrise the next day, when the Farmer and his son cut down the grain, they found an empty nest.

Self-help is the best help.

The Fisherman
and the Little Fish

There once was a poor Fisherman who lived only on the fish he caught. One day, he had bad luck and caught nothing but a little Fish. The Fisherman was about to put it in his basket when the little Fish said:

"Please let me go, Mr. Fisherman! I am so small I would make no meal at all for you. When I am bigger, I shall make you a much better meal."

But the Fisherman quickly put the Fish into his basket.

"How foolish I would be," he said, "to throw you back. You may be little, but you are better than nothing at all."

A small gain is worth more
than a large promise.

The Fighting Roosters

Once there were two Roosters living in the same farmyard. They could not bear the sight of each other. At last one day they flew up to fight it out, beak and claw. They fought until one of them was beaten and crawled off to a corner to hide.

The winning Rooster flew to the top of the henhouse. He proudly flapped his wings and crowed with all his might to tell the world about his victory. An Eagle heard the loud crowing. She swooped down and carried him off to her nest.

The Rooster who had lost the battle looked up and saw the Eagle fly off. And so, he came out of his corner and took his place as master of the farmyard.

Pride goes before a fall.

The Two Pots

There were once two Pots that stood together near the fireplace. One Pot was made of brass. The other was made of clay.

One day the Brass Pot said to the Clay Pot, "We should have an adventure. Let's go out into the world together."

But the Clay Pot said, "Oh, dear, no. I am safer here at home in this corner by the fire. I am made of clay. It would take so little to break me. One bump is sure to shatter me!"

"Don't let that keep you at home," said the Brass Pot. "I will take very good care of you. If we happen to meet anything hard, I will step between and save you."

So the Clay Pot at last agreed and the two Pots set out side by side. They waddled along on three stubby legs, first to this side, then to that, and bumping into each other at every step.

The Clay Pot could not last long with this "bumpy" friendship. They had only gone about ten steps when a bump from the Brass Pot made the Clay Pot crack. After just a few more waddling steps—and bumps—the poor Clay Pot shattered into a hundred pieces.

It's usually best if friends are equally matched.

The Owl and the Grasshopper

The old Owl always slept during the day. Then after sundown, when shadows rose slowly through the woods, out she came from her old hollow tree. "*Hoo-hoo-hoo-oo-oo*," she called, ruffling her feathers. Then she began her hunt for the bugs, beetles, frogs, and mice she liked to eat.

Now, this old Owl had become very cross and hard to please as she grew older. She did not like for anything to wake her while she slept. One warm summer afternoon, as the Owl dozed away in her old oak tree, a Grasshopper nearby began a joyous song. Out popped the Owl's head from the tree.

"Whoooo is making that noise? Get away from here," she said to the Grasshopper. "Have you no manners? You should respect my age and leave me to sleep in quiet!"

"I have a right to this place in the sun!" snapped the Grasshopper. "And I will make music if I want to!" With that, he began to play his song again.

The wise old Owl knew it would do no good to argue with the Grasshopper. So she decided not to speak angry words. Instead, she spoke softly and kindly to him.

"Well, sir," she said, "if I *must* stay awake, I am going to settle down to enjoy your music. Now that I think of it, I have a wonderful honey tea here, sent to me from the gods. I am told that Apollo, the god of music, drinks this tea before he sings and plays the harp. Please come up and taste this tea with me. I know it will make you sound like Apollo himself, for you are a master at music."

The foolish Grasshopper was flattered by the Owl's words. Up he jumped to the Owl's den. But as soon as he was near enough, the old Owl pounced upon him and ate him up.

Beware sweet words that drip with honey.

The Kid and the Wolf

A little Kid was nibbling grass with the rest of the flock. However, he stayed too long in one spot and the flock moved on with the shepherd without him. The little Kid became afraid. He called for his mother—but who should hear him, but a Wolf!

The Wolf jumped out from behind a tree. The Kid knew there was little hope for him.

"Please, Mr. Wolf," he said, "I know you are going to kill me. And I know that after your cruel work, you play a lively tune on your pipe before you eat. No one is a better piper than you. Please, may I hear your tune before you kill me?—for I want to dance and be merry as long as I can."

The Wolf was flattered. He took his pipe and played a merry tune while he watched his meal dance about merrily.

Meanwhile, the shepherd's Dogs heard the tune. "The Wolf pipes before he eats!" said one. They raced toward the sound and in a moment they were upon the Wolf. The Wolf dropped his pipe and ran away, losing his pipe and his meal.

Finish your work before you play.

The Turtle and the Ducks

A Turtle looked around at the chipmunks and rabbits. "How I wish I could scamper about like that," he said. He looked up at the birds overhead. "How I wish I could soar like that," he sighed.

One day the Turtle was grumbling to some Ducks, "Life is not fair. You have wings. I must lug this heavy shell about. If I did not have this awful shell, I would be able to see the world."

"We can help you see the world," said the Ducks. "Take hold of this stick with your mouth. We will carry you far up in the air to see everywhere."

The Turtle was happy to try this. He clamped down tightly onto the stick. The two Ducks took hold, and away they sailed up toward the clouds.

A Crow flew by who was shocked to see a flying Turtle. "Is this the King of Turtles?" he cried.

"Why, yes, I—" began the Turtle.

But as he opened his mouth to say these foolish words, he lost his hold on the stick. And down, down he fell, hitting the ground with a thud. The only thing that saved him was his "awful" shell.

Be thankful for the gifts you have.

The Monkey and the Camel

The animals of the forest held a grand party in honor of King Lion. The Monkey was asked to dance. His dancing was very clever indeed, and the king enjoyed his lively steps.

The animals cheered and praised the Monkey, and this made the Camel jealous. He was sure that he could dance as well as the Monkey, if not better. He pushed his way forward, rose up on his hind legs, and began to dance. But the big, clumsy Camel looked foolish as he kicked out his knotty legs and twisted his long neck. He even stepped on the toes of some of the animals.

At last one of his huge feet came within an inch of King Lion's nose! The animals were so disgusted that they set upon the Camel in a rage and drove him out into the desert.

Enjoy—don't envy—the talents of others.

The Mice and the Weasels

The Weasels and the Mice were always battling each other. The winners of every battle were the Weasels, who carried off some of the Mice to have for dinner.

The Mice, of course, were very upset. They called a meeting and decided that the Mouse army needed some leaders. So several Mice were made generals. "We must wear something that shows we are important," said the generals. And so the Mice made them hats with tall feathers. At last they felt ready for war, and they sent a challenge to the Weasels.

The Weasels were always ready for a fight and they attacked the Mice. The poor Mice were losing again, and they all ran for their mouse holes. But the Mouse generals could not squeeze through their little doorways because of their tall feathers. And the Weasels once again dined on Mice that day.

Leadership often comes
with its own set of problems.

The Wolf and the Goat

A hungry Wolf saw a Goat nibbling grass at the top of a steep cliff. *I cannot reach her up there*, thought the Wolf.

"That is a very dangerous place for you," he called out, pretending to be worried about the Goat's safety. "What if you should fall? Please listen to me and come down! Here you can get all you want of the most tender grass in the country."

The Goat looked over the edge of the cliff.

"How very, very concerned you are about me," she said, "and how kind of you to offer your grass! But I know you! You're not concerned about what *I* will eat. You're only thinking about what *you* want to eat—me!"

Beware invitations from the selfish.

The Peacock and the Crane

A proud Peacock met a Crane one day. The Peacock wanted to impress him, so he spread his gorgeous tail in the sun.

"Look," he said. "What do you have to compare with this? I am dressed in all the glory of the rainbow, while your feathers are gray as dust!"

The Crane spread his broad wings and flew up toward the sun.

"Follow me if you can," he said.

But the Peacock stood where he was among the birds of the barnyard, while the Crane soared in freedom far up into the blue sky.

When the beautiful is not useful,
it has very little value.

The Man and the Faun

A Man met a Faun in the forest. He tried to become friends with the Faun, but the Faun said that Men were foolish, senseless creatures.

"Come have dinner with me, and you shall see that Men are indeed sensible," said the Man.

As they walked to the Man's hut, the cold wind was blowing. The Man began to blow on his fingers.

"Why do you do that?" asked the Faun.

"To warm my hands," the Man replied.

When they reached home, the Man made two bowls of hot soup. As the Faun and the Man sat down to enjoy the meal, the Man began to blow into his bowl of soup.

"Why do you do that?" asked the Faun.

"To cool my soup," replied the Man.

The Faun sprang to his feet and ran to the door.

"Good-bye," he said. "I've seen enough. A fellow that blows hot and cold in the same breath cannot be friends with me!"

What is sensible to one
may be foolishness to another.

The Lion and the Bulls

A Lion saw three Bulls feeding in a field. He attacked them several times, but they kept together and drove him off. The Lion was no match for three Bulls with sharp horns.

Then one day the Bulls had a quarrel. When the Lion came to look at them and lick his chops, he found them in separate corners of the field. It was now easy for the Lion to attack them one at a time, for they no longer could fight him together.

United, you stand. Divided, you fall.

The Dogs and the Hides

Four Dogs saw some deer hides at the bottom of a stream where a hunter had put them to soak.

"An excellent meal for us," said one Dog. "But how can we reach them?"

"Let us drink up the stream!" said another.

So the four began lapping up the water as fast as they could. They drank and drank until they became ill—and the water in the stream was as high as ever.

Do not try to do the impossible.

The Bat and the Weasels

A Bat lost his way and flew into the nest of a Weasel. The hungry Weasel caught him. The Bat begged for his life, but the Weasel would not listen.

"You are a Mouse," he said, "and I am an enemy of Mice. Every Mouse I catch, I am going to eat!"

"But I am not a Mouse!" cried the Bat. "Look at my wings. Can Mice fly? Why, I am only a Bird! Please let me go."

The Weasel had to admit that the Bat was not a Mouse, so he let him go. But a few days later, the foolish Bat went blindly into the nest of another Weasel. This Weasel happened to eat Birds. He soon had the Bat under his claws, ready to eat him.

"Ah! A Bird!" he said. "I have my dinner!"

"What?" cried the Bat. "You think I am a Bird? Why, all Birds have feathers! I am nothing but a Mouse. Please let me go."

The Weasel had to admit that the Bat was not a Bird, so he let him go. And the Bat escaped with his life a second time.

Turn events to your best advantage.

The Fox and the Leopard

A Fox and a Leopard were resting lazily after a good dinner. The Leopard groomed his fine, spotted coat. He looked over at the plain coat of the Fox and gave a smirk and a small laugh.

Now, the Fox knew he would never look as fine as the Leopard. And he very much wanted to be his friend. *I can entertain him with my wit and funny stories*, he thought.

The Fox began to tell the Leopard some funny stories about his crafty tricks and wily ways. He kept waiting for the Leopard to laugh. But the Leopard just looked blankly at the Fox. He did not understand the meaning of any of the Fox's jokes and witty stories.

At last the Fox decided to leave. "You have a very smart coat," he said to the Leopard. "But it's hard to be friends with someone with no smarts inside his head. I would rather have a fine friend than a friend with just fine looks."

A true friend laughs with you, not at you.

INDEX OF FABLES

INDEX OF FABLES